Table of Contents

Workbook
9

Listen. Read. Write.
Vowel

long **O**

Look at this word search.
Find and circle all of the words that have
the long vowel sound of **o** as in **yo-yo**.
The words may be down or across.

w	u	t	i	n
h	e	l	l	o
a	c	a	n	x
s	o	g	u	f
v	r	o	c	y

I am small and
round and taste
good with butter.

My name has the
sound of **long o**.

2

Look at the picture.
Write the word that names the picture.
Circle a word that rhymes with it.

draw

pillow 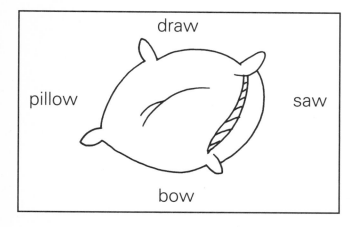 saw

bow

_____

- - - - - - - - - - - - -

_____

call

low 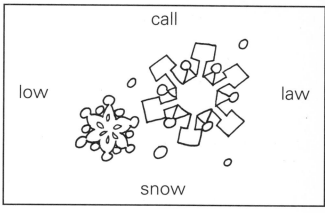 law

snow

_____

- - - - - - - - - - - - -

_____

hot

slow  stall

crow

_____

- - - - - - - - - - - - -

_____

blow

wall  saw

below

_____

- - - - - - - - - - - - -

_____

I have many
colors.
You see me
after it rains.

What is the
opposite of
fast?

Unscramble the letters to make new words.
Write the words. Circle the words whose names have
the sounds of **ow** as in **bow**.

o c r w _____

o s w h _____

y w n a _____

c a l w _____

l g w o _____

l w o f _____

g r w o _____

w l o _____

What do you
do with
bubble gum?

What do
you put
soup in?

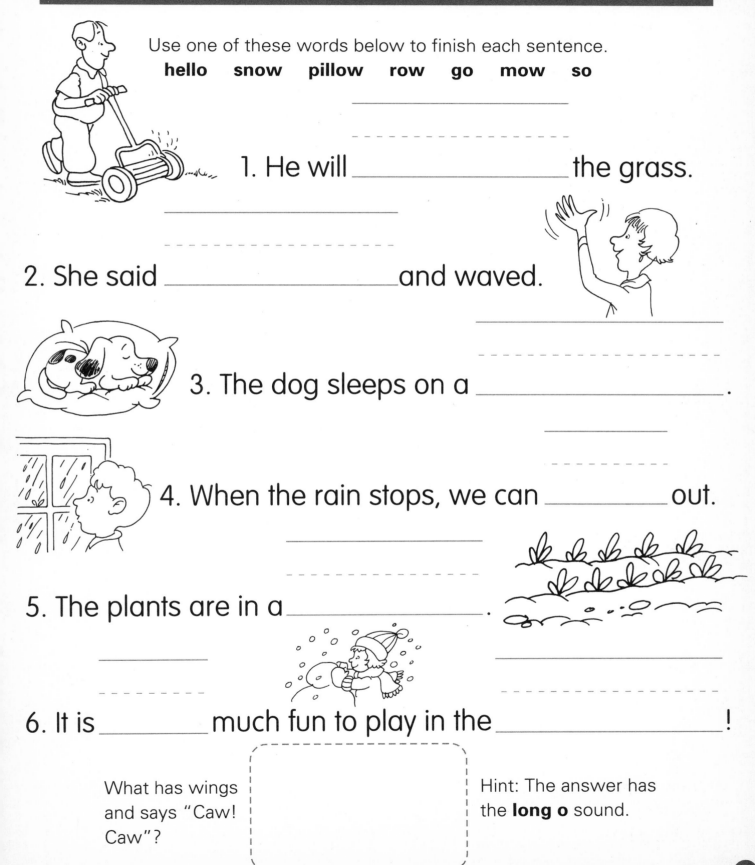

Use one of these words below to finish each sentence.

hello   snow   pillow   row   go   mow   so

1. He will _____ the grass.

2. She said _____ and waved.

3. The dog sleeps on a _____.

4. When the rain stops, we can _____ out.

5. The plants are in a _____.

6. It is _____ much fun to play in the _____!

What has wings and says "Caw! Caw"?

Hint: The answer has the **long o** sound.

Write one of the words below to finish each sentence.

air   away   answer   learn   world

I like to _____ things in class.

This is the _____.

He knows the _____.

I will go _____ for a week.

He blows it up with _____.

Phonics Reader 25: *Rainbows*

Think about the book you read called *Rainbows*. Look at these pictures from the book. Write in a word to finish each sentence.

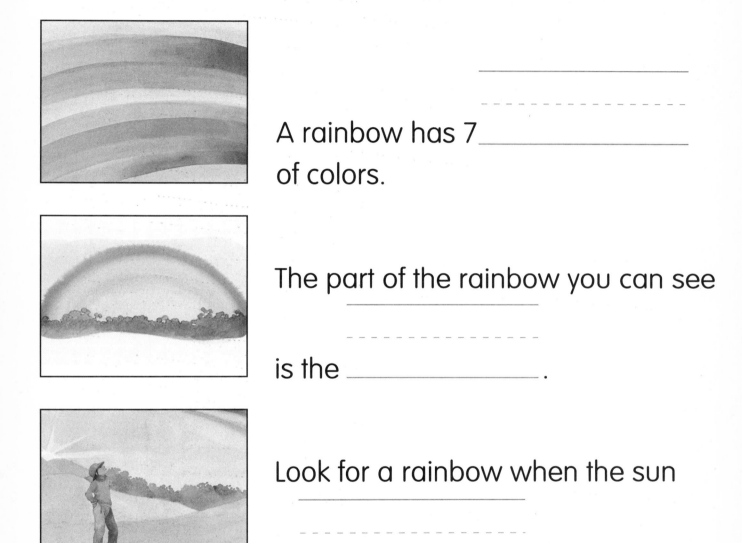

A rainbow has 7 _____ of colors.

The part of the rainbow you can see _____ is the _____.

Look for a rainbow when the sun _____ is _____.

A rainbow _____ around the moon when it rains.

long **e**
(y)

Draw a line from the picture to its name. Which picture names end with the sound of **long e** as in **baby**? Write those words on the lines next to the pictures.

body

hay

penny

candy

clay

pony

I am a small red fruit.

I am the opposite of sad.

Make a poem. Use one of these words to finish the sentences.

guppy**bunny****puppy****funny**

_____

- - - - - - - - - - - - - - - - - - -

The baby dog is a _____.

_____

- - - - - - - - - - - - - - - - - - -

The baby fish is a _____.

_____

- - - - - - - - - - - - - - - - - - -

The baby rabbit is a _____.

_____

- - - - - - - - - - - - - - - - - - -

See them play. They are all so _____!

How do you feel before a meal?	What comes next? 10, 20, 30, 40,	Hint: Both answers end with the **long e** sound.

long **e**
(ey)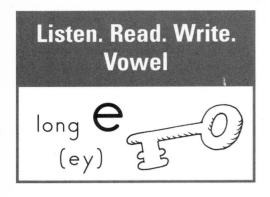

Look at each picture.
Write **ey** on the line if the picture name has
the **long e** sound as in **key**.

Bees make it.
We eat it.

Hint: The answer
ends in the sound
of **ey**.

Phonics Reader 26: *Plum's Paint Brush*

Look at the secret code below. A number stands for a letter. Use the secret code to write words that have the **long o** sound of **oa** as in **coat**.

long O
(oa)

0	1	2	3	4	5	6	7	8	9	10
a	b	d	f	l	m	n	o	s	t	g

1. 10 7 0 9

2. 3 4 7 0 9

3. 7 0 9

4. 9 7 0 2

5. 10 7 0 4

6. 1 7 0 9

7. 9 7 0 8 9

8. 4 7 0 2

You use me
to get clean.

Look at the pictures. Circle the word or words that finishes the sentence.

He thinks that is **fine funny**.

The **bone boat** is on the lake.

The **key keep** locks the door.

The **road rope** is wide.

The **baby bib** has on a **baby bib**.

The **toad turkey** is fat.

I am an animal whose name rhymes with coat.

Look at each picture. Use one of the words below to finish each sentence.

animals   house   picture   point   study

She can draw a _____ .

He will _____ to a place on the map.

This is my _____ .

Bob needs to _____ for his test.

These _____ live at my house.

The pictures from the story *Plum's Paint Brush* are out of order.
Put them in story order by writing 1, 2, 3, or 4 under each picture.

_____

- - - - - - - - -

_____

_____

- - - - - - - - -

_____

_____

- - - - - - - - -

_____

_____

- - - - - - - - -

_____

All these words have the sound of **oo** as in **foot**. Read the clues. Then use one of the words below to fill in the crossword puzzle.

crook   hoof   book   good   brook   hood

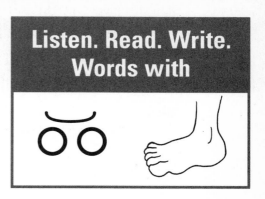

Down
1. the opposite of bad
2. an animal foot
3. a small stream

Across
2. part of a coat that goes over the head
3. you read this
4. someone who steals

This comes from sheep. Sweaters are made from it.

Use these words to write a sentence about each picture.

foot   cook   looked   wood

What is at the
end of a fishing
pole?

Read the two words. Which has the sound of **oo** as in **moon**? Use that word to finish the sentence.

steal
stool   She sat on the _____.

food
fade   My plate has _____ on it.

zip
zoo   We saw an ape at the _____.

scoop
skip   He has one _____ of ice cream.

hoop
hip   He tossed the ball into the _____.

books
boots   I put on my _____.

What goes
with a knife
and fork?

You blow me
up and tie me
to a string.
What am I?

Look at this word puzzle.

Find and circle all of the words that have the sound of **oo** as in **moon**.

They may be down, across, or side to side.

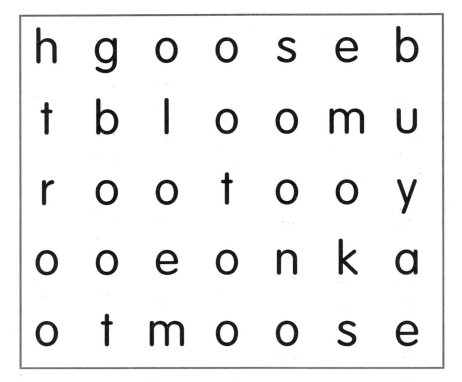

You can sweep
with me.

Let's Review Words with $\overline{\text{oo}}$

Say the name of each picture.
Circle the word that rhymes with the picture name.

stood
stand

sun
soon

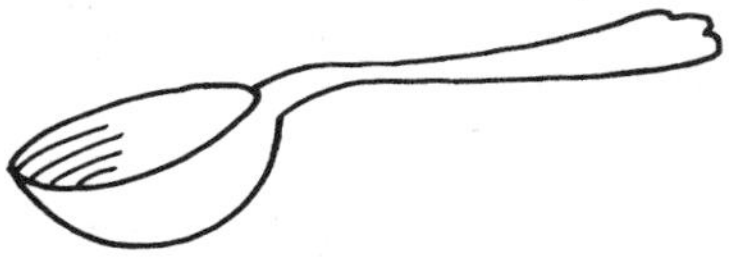

lace
loose

look
like

zoom
blame

rude
root

take
took

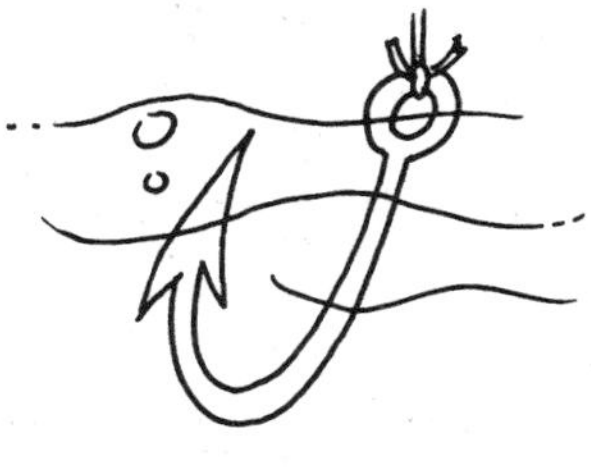

good
glide

tool
tale

shook
shake

Make a comic strip.
Use one of the words below to finish each sentence.

also   even   help   should   through

"I think we _____ have a snack."

"I would _____ like a snack."

"Let's go _____ this hole."

"Stop! I do not think you will _____
fit through the hole."

"I'm stuck. _____!"

Think about the story you read called *Food*.
Write a sentence that tells something about each picture.

Test Yourself!

Underline the word that names each picture. Then write the word on the line.

1. Peas need sun to _____ .
goat, goal, grow

2. The _____ is in the door.
key, keep, keg

3. This _____ feels nice.
cat, coat, cute

4. The _____ has dots.
bow, boom, ball

5. She is _____ .
hope, happy, help

6. I like to ride the _____ .
ducky, doggy, donkey

Test Yourself!

Fill in the circle next to the word that best finishes each sentence.
Write the word on the line.

1. This plant has a _____ .
rate, root, rot

2. The _____ makes her face clean.
sap, sob, soap

3. We will _____ into the pool.
go, goal, glow

4. She stood on her left _____ .
feet, food, foot

5. I will use my _____ to eat.
spoon, spun, spin

6. He has _____ for the fire.
wide, wood, weed

Answer Key

PAGE 2

PAGE 3 pillow/bow; snow/low; crow/slow; blow/below

PAGE 4 crow; show; yawn; claw; glow; flow; grow; low

PAGE 5 mow; hello; pillow; go; row; so; snow

PAGE 6 learn, world, answer, away, air

PAGE 7 rows, bow, low, glows

PAGE 8 body, penny, candy, pony

PAGE 9 puppy; guppy; bunny; funny

PAGE 10 donkey, chimney, monkey

PAGE 11 goat; float; oat; toad; goal; boat; toast; load

PAGE 12 funny, boat, key, road, baby/bib, turkey

PAGE 13 picture, point, house, study, animals

PAGE 14 2, 4, 3, 1

PAGE 15 *down:* 1. good, 2. hoof, 3. brook
across: 2. hood, 3. book, 4. crook

PAGE 16 answers will vary

PAGE 17 stool, food, zoo, scoop, hoop, boots

PAGE 18

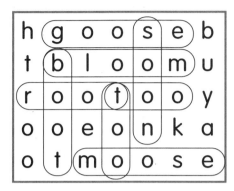

PAGE 19 stood; soon; loose; look; zoom; root; took; good; tool; shook

PAGE 20 should, also, through, even, Help

PAGE 21 sentences will vary

PAGE 22 1. grow
2. key
3. coat
4. bow
5. happy
6. donkey

PAGE 23 1. root
2. soap
3. go
4. foot
5. spoon
6. wood